THE GOOD CONDOM GUIDE

by Leonard Stall

Illustrated by
Aardvark Design Studio

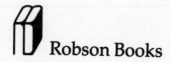

Robson Books

First published in Great Britain in 1992 by
Robson Books Ltd, Bolsover House,
5-6 Clipstone Street, London W1P 7EB

British Library Cataloguing in Publication Data
A catalogue record for this book is available
from the British Library

ISBN 0 86051 828 0

Printed and bound in Great Britain by
Butler & Tanner Ltd,
Frome and London

LOVE YOUR CONDOM

James Tye, Chairman
National Condom Week Campaign/British Safety Council

You'll remember the bewildering Government funded 'Awareness' TV adverts of five years ago featuring icebergs crumbling into the sea and like me you will probably have asked yourself 'What the hell have crumbling icebergs got to do with not catching AIDS?' Subsequent Government 'Prevent AIDS' advertising campaigns have been similarly condemned as being ineffective, underlining the old adage that 'Half of advertising is a waste of money'.

Talk to advertising men away from the market survey wiz kids and they agree with us that until there is a drug or a shot in the arm which will prevent or cure AIDS the best solution is to use condoms. We translated that into 'Love your condom' and have featured 'Love your condom', 'Cover up', 'Cover it up' and this year's 'Slip into Something Safe and Sexy' with 'Carry-on' star Barbara Windsor.

In the last five years I have welcomed the changes in attitudes to condoms. No longer considered a taboo subject, condoms have definitely come out of the closet.

Amazing really to think that the condom has been around since Ancient Times and yet its value has never been more relevant than at present.

Of course, we are pleased that the Americans, Canadians, Aussies and others have been quick to copy our National Condom Week campaigns, even using our posters and promotion materials (there is no charge), as its just as important to love the condom in New York, Melbourne and Saskatchewan as in London, Paris or Tokyo.

Latest Department of Health figures show an alarming increase in sexually transmitted diseases (including AIDS).

At last then, a simple, straightforward and entertaining guide to the condom. *The Good Condom Guide* provides detailed and up-to-date information on everything you will ever want to know about the condom and more besides.

I firmly believe that you can get more messages over to people with a smile than ever with a frown and this *Good Condom Guide* certainly achieves that. I wish it well.

THE GOOD CONDOM GUIDE
CONTENTS

We don't want anybody in the Condom Club - *just large members!*

Welcome to The Good Condom Guide, or 'Everything You've Ever Wanted To Know About Your Mates!'

We've had a lot of fun writing and compiling this definitive work on rubber johnnies, and hope that the information, stories, jokes and fascinating facts whet your appetite for getting to know even more about our remarkable subject matter first hand.

And, we also hope that The Good Condom Guide Ratings we have given every condom featured in this book, help point you in the right direction.

There are so many people to thank for their help with this sticky matter that it would be impossible to list them all.

During the exhausting testing and marking process, we barely slept, and some of our staff literally refused to lie down before the job was done. They know what it's like to have their backs up against the wall under pressure!

An estimated 45 million couples use condoms around the world, and that figure is growing all the time.

We hope that this book will encourage a few more to join the Users Club, which has a new motto: 'It's safe in the bag'.

'Use a condom and you will learn, no deposit, no return!'
Slogan from USA.

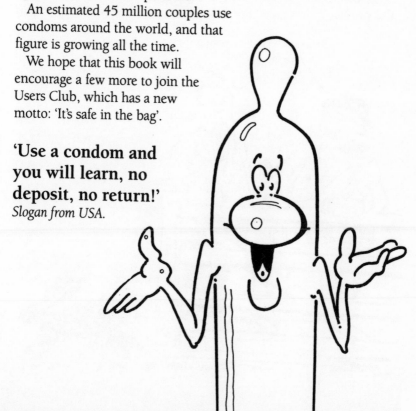

HISTORY

THE HISTORY OF THE JOHNNY ...
AND THE JOHNNY IN HISTORY

The 'barrier method' of contraception probably dates back to Roman times when animal bladders were used, mainly to prevent the spread of sexually transmitted diseases.

The invention of the condom came much later, or so they say.

Folklore suggests that a physician at the court of Charles II named Dr Condom made the johnny breakthrough.

But, it is more likely that the word originated from the Latin word for receptacle, 'condus', being used as a euphemism for an item already well known and well used.

Italian anatomist Gabriel Fallopio is on the record as the first person to publish a description of a sheath way back in 1564. He favoured a linen sheath moistened with lotion to protect the wearer against the perils of VD. At this time condoms were normally made of animal intestines.

The condom revolution came in 1844 when Messrs Hancock and Goodyear developed the vulcanisation of rubber.

"Haven't you ever seen a pubic hare!"

*"Mr Philips is rather lowering
the tone of the area."*

FIRST COME, FIRST SERVE

The first commercial condoms went on sale from a wholesale
outlet in Half Moon Street, London in the 1700s.

The proprietor was a well known lady called Mrs Philips who
ran an international business from her premises, winning
customers over with ingenious rhyming sales pitches:

'To guard yourself from shame or fear
Votaries to Venus hasten here
None in my way e'er found a flaw
Self preservation's nature's law'.

By the end of the century Mrs Philips had some 35 years'
experience in the condom business, supplying customers from
chemists to ambassadors, 'foreigners to gentlemen'!

She boasted that her condoms were the 'best goods in England,
and on the shortest notice at the lowest price'.

300 CONDOMS FOR THE FRISKY FRENCH KING

Louis XV of France was a fan of the condom, and British condoms in particular.

According to a letter dated April 26 1749, recently uncovered by top history magazine *History Today*, the secretary of the British Embassy at the time Colonel Joseph York was asked to help obtain British condoms for the frisky French King.

The letter reveals that Louis was so worried about his mistresses bearing children that he had an aide ask York to 'procure around 300 preventive machines' from England, as French Letters were obviously not yet made in France!

RESIST THAT!

In 1916, Rome decreed that any wife who had to face her husband wearing a condom 'must resist him as she would a rapist'.

"Mon dieu my King, they have sold out in duty free."

"Casanova - are those your sheep outside?"

SAFE SEX THROUGH THE AGES

The great Casanova who lived from 1725-1798, widely believed to have been the world's most prolific lover, used sheep-gut condoms to keep himself and his mistresses out of trouble.

In the absence of condoms as we know and love them today, lovers in history were well used to wearing animal membranes for safe sex.

Goats' bladders were popular in ancient Crete, and the Romans also favoured animal bladders.

Indeed, the term French Letter is probably a corruption of 'French Bladder' - condoms made from sheep's intestines, which were once imported in great quantities across the Channel to stop the spread of venereal disease.

Skin condoms are still available today made from the caeca of lambs.

Real skin condoms are said to ensure greater sensitivity, as the animal membrane is a better conductor of heat than rubber.

But, while skin condoms are still available and popular in some corners of the globe, the science of contraception has moved on and the condoms of the 1990s are safer and sexier than ever before.

BLOW ME DOWN!

Casanova, the world's greatest and best known lover, called condoms the 'English Riding Coat...the English vestment that puts one's mind at rest'.

He is said to have individually tested all the condoms he used for holes by blowing them up like balloons!

"I didn't come here tonight just to watch you blow up balloons."

"She kept on sneezing - I couldn't decide if it was passion or she just had a terrible cold!"

MILESTONES IN CONTRACEPTION

A clever Roman doctor called Soranos was one of the first men in history to make a study of contraception.

He decided the best 'anti-baby' method was for the woman to hold her breath when her partner ejaculated, and afterwards to sneeze violently.

Elephant dung was particularly popular among the Persians in the tenth century. That well-known writer of the time Rhazes, recommended rolled-up balls of elephant dung as the best method of contraception.

The Egyptians went one better in the field of contraception, having a penchant for crocodile dung pessaries.

Other popular contraceptives over the years have included:
* Eating Bees
* Washing the penis in vinegar
* Wearing a cat's testicles in a container around the waist, and more recently,
* Using Coca-Cola as a douche - Diet Coke is said to be the best!

Of late however, the condom seems to have captured the market....

ON THE JOB

HOW TO USE A CONDOM:
USEFUL POINTS TO REMEMBER.

* Wear a new condom every time you make love, and put the condom on before any sexual contact takes place.

* Check the expiry date on the condom packet before use.

* Remove the condom from the packet, being careful not to damage it with your fingernail or jewellery.

* Pinch the nipple end
or teat (the closed end)
of the condom with
your thumb and
forefinger to expel the
air. This will be the
'reservoir' for the semen
after ejaculation.

ON THE JOB

* Roll the condom down the entire length of the erect penis, keeping it air free. Do not try to put a condom on a flaccid penis!

* After love-making, remove the penis from the vagina holding the condom around the base of the penis so that it remains in place and no semen escapes.

* Dispose of your used condom hygienically.

SAFE SEX - HOW CONDOMS ARE MADE

Condoms are made on a production line.

Condom-shaped metal or glass moulds are dipped into a latex solution, and then pass through a drying oven.

After immersion in latex, the moulds then pass through another heated chamber for drying and vulcanisation.

The end products are usually rolled off the moulds by nylon brushes, and then rigorously tested.

THE TRUTH ABOUT CONDOMS

* A typical condom can hold around 40 litres of air before bursting.

* The UK manufactured Durex brand can stretch to a length of 40 inches, and a width of 12 inches. That should be big enough for any man! In fact, a Durex condom could almost accommodate a whale's penis!

* Modern latex condoms can be as little as 0.0016 inches thick.

* Condoms have a shelf life of at least five years, but can deteriorate quickly in unusual conditions such as the heat and humidity of the Tropics.

* Baby oil, petroleum jelly and corn oil can strip a condom of some 92% of its strength in under 15 minutes according to the Consumers Association. And, thicker condoms are just as vulnerable as thin ones.

"Well they make one to fit a whale ..."

"Don't you think you've overdone the spermicide foam?"

CONDOM TIPS

The 4ml of an average man's ejaculate can easily contain 300 million sperm, and a minute proportion of this can cause pregnancy.

So, to get the best from your condom take care to use it properly and carefully.

Don't:
* make genital contact before putting on your condom.
* put on your condom just before ejaculation. It may then be too late to catch that crucial first fraction of sperm - the sperm that does the damage!
* damage the condom before use.
* make accidental genital contact with your partner when there is sperm on the penis from earlier intercourse, before a new condom is put on.
* use oil based lubricants in conjunction with your condom.
* leak on withdrawal!

Do:
* use good quality condoms.
* use a new condom every time you make love.
* use condoms in conjunction with spermicide for the best results.
* arrange postcoital contraception within three days if a condom slips off or splits during intercourse.

NO IDEA!

Leading women's magazine *Cosmopolitan* asked 50 men under 35 years of age, nearly all of them living with a partner, how reliable they think the condom is as a method of contraception. Incredible as it may seem, 72% of them had no idea.

Many quoted figures which ranged from 70% reliable to 99% reliable.

And, when *Cosmo* asked what the figures actually refer to the men in the survey hadn't a clue.

"If you sleep with a woman 100 times she'll get pregnant 30 times," said one man who reckoned condoms were 70% reliable! That man should have fathered around 100 children by now if he is right.

For the record, condom manufacturers now claim that their products are 98% reliable. That means for every 100 women who use a condom every time they make love for a year, only two will become pregnant.

"Actually I'm on level 5."

But, failure rates can vary enormously, depending on the care taken by the users.

According to J Guillbaud's revealing book *Contraception: Your Questions Answered*, they can be as low as 0.4 pregnancies/100 woman years, a figure recorded in the north of England in 1973. On the other hand in 1961 a survey in Puerto Rico recorded a failure rate as high as 32 pregnancies/100 woman years.

SIGN OF THE TIMES
Switzerland, October 1990: Around 40% of sexually active people in the 17-30 year old age group reported using condoms 'consistently'.

In 1987 only 8% had reported 'consistently' using condoms.

LET'S PLAY IT SAFE.
The condom provides a level of protection against:
* Aids
* Gonorrhoea
* Trichomonas vaginitis
   It probably also protects against the spirochaete of syphilis, Chlamydia, and similar bacterial and protozoal organisms.

But, since herpes virus lesions often cover a wide area, the condom may not be as good a form of protection as some believe.

"What do you prefer Darling - condoms or bunk beds?"

MEASURING UP

PAN-EUROPEAN GUIDELINES

An independent committee of experts led by the London International Group - the manufacturer of the Durex brand - has been deciding on pan-European guidelines for condoms in the 'Single Market', including the minimum length and the maximum width.

A recent memo from the Eurocrats entitled 'Safe Sex In A Single Market' stresses that inferior quality condoms could have 'disastrous consequences', and reiterates that all 12 EC governments asked the Commission to ensure that condoms are manufactured to the necessary standards.

The Eurocrats have been super sensitive on the condoms issue after a spate of ridicule for their efforts in other directions.

One which captured the public eye was a directive that was sent out on the correct curve for cucumbers, and there have already been disputes about Swiss Rolls that don't come from Switzerland, and Brussel Sprouts that don't come from Brussels!

"So then the French objected to the use of French letter."

HUMOUR

BILL OF FARE

Checking in for the celebrity launch of Euro Disney, the newlywed Donald and Daisy Duck ordered special honeymoon cocktails from the hotel bar and waddled back to their room.

Daisy slipped into something more comfortable and jumped onto the huge double bed. As she cuddled up to her new husband, she asked: "Don't you think you ought to use a condom darling?"

Unprepared, as ever, Donald rang down to the hotel reception and asked room service to send him up a packet of condoms as soon as they possibly could.

"Would you like them put on your bill, sir?" asked the telephonist.

"You must be joking," replied Donald. "What do you think I am, some kind of pervert!"

DIE HARD

An Englishman, Scotsman and Irishman are sentenced to death, but are allowed to choose the way they die as a last wish.

"I would like to be executed by hanging," said the Englishman. "It's a traditional and very honourable way to die where I come from." He was later hanged till dead, as he had asked.

"I would like to be shot straight between the eyes," said the Scotsman. "Quick, with no pain - that's the way I want it."

He was shot, and died instantly.

"I would like to die of Aids," said the Irishman.

After being given Aids by his squad of executioners, the Irishman began laughing uncontrollably.

"I have cheated death," he cried.

Amazed by the man's remarkable and ridiculous outburst, the executioner asked how.

"I was wearing a condom!"

RUGGER BUGGER

Such has been the dramatic decline in the fortunes of the Welsh national rugby team that in order to fill up the seats at the home ground, Cardiff Arms Park, tickets for internationals are now having to be sold in chemists.

On a recent visit to Wales to see my friend Dai, I spotted a poster advertising tickets for the Wales v England match in one chemist's window. "Look Dai," I said. "Go in and get a couple of tickets for Saturday's match will you?"

Reluctantly he agreed, in an effort to please his long-standing friend from London.

He returned 20 minutes later with two packets of condoms. "I was far too embarrassed to ask for the tickets!" he winced.

"You did say two tickets sir."

WHAT A BUMMER

Did you hear about the gay condom who was invited to go on holiday?

He turned the offer down because he didn't want to leave his friends behind!

NOBBLED

Do you know what the nipple on the end of a condom is actually for?

It's to put your foot on when you're taking it off!

"So you reckon if I bite this I'll know what to do with those."

TYRED OUT
What do you do with 365 used condoms?

Roll them into a tyre, and call it a 'Good Year'.

TON UP
An athletic looking young man goes into a leading high street chemist and asks the sales assistant for 99 condoms.
"F**k me," she says, aghast at the man's obvious prowess.
"You'd better make that 100 then please!" replies the delighted customer.

MUSIC TO MY EARS
Is that Johnny Rotten?

No, I've only used it once!

"It stayed on all the way through just like I was shown."

NUN FUN

The Mother Superior stood up in front of the 100 nuns in her convent, and scowled.

"Sisters, I am dismayed. Evil is among us. I have found a condom in this house of God...."

As she spoke, 99 nuns gasped, and one giggled.

The Mother Superior continued...."What's more, Sisters. I have to tell you that this contraceptive device had a hole in it!"

99 nuns giggled, one gasped.

"I haven't seen one of those since Beni Dictus ..."

THE GOOD CONDOM GUIDE

- THE BRANDS WE EXAMINED

The Guide looked at a large number of top brands from around the world, scoring the condoms with a Good Condom Guide Rating, and providing some extra details where we could.

Brand Name: A real giveaway as to the type of product you're getting. At one end of the spectrum we purchased an 'Anti Baby' condom, and at the other a novelty brand named Licks!

Manufacturer: We list the manufacturer where the packet indicates who this is. Not all do. Some credit the importer or the agency/company marketing the product, and others make no mention of who, or where the condom has come from.

Packaging: In most cases the packaging gives a good indication of what you can expect inside.

CONDOM

SUPER SENSITIVE

- THE BRANDS WE EXAMINED

Today condom brands are often specifically targeted; either at married users, singles, the gay community, or just at buyers looking for a novelty product to give as presents, or give a little 'je ne sais quoi' to proceedings.

Suffice to say, there are some companies around the world who package their products imaginatively, but many more who don't! Packaging is becoming more and more important.

Special Features: Variety is the spice of life. Among the mainstream brands spermicidal lubricant is becoming more and more the norm. But, there are plenty of other features among today's international condoms to tickle your fancy: different ribs, dots, colours, shapes, and flavours. Smell that burning rubber! Some are stronger, longer, and some smaller and thinner. There are also condoms with stimulants, succulents, de-sensitisers, even patterns, and real skin brands are available.

Good Condom Guide Rating: There are four badges the condoms can earn in our penetrating survey, not surprisingly the Four F's; *Flamboyant, Fun, Functional* and *Feeble*.

Flamboyant - Only for the most exotic and erotic condoms, but please note these are not necessarily the safest and most reliable.

Fun - For those brands that put a smile on our face during the stiff testing. Again an award for pleasure and not necessarily for the safest and most reliable brands.

Functional - All of the properly tested 'sensible' brands earn this Guide merit award for johnny excellence.

Feeble - Uninspiring. Hardly worth getting excited about in our opinion.

* Form-Fit: condoms that are contoured to fit the head of the penis.
* Teat end: also called the nipple, and reservoir. The area at the closed end of the condom used to collect the semen after ejaculation, which might otherwise seep down the length of the condom.
* Ribbed: raised ribs manufactured as an integral part of the condom, and designed to give extra stimulation during intercourse. Raised dots and studs are also a feature of some condoms.
* Flavour: some condoms are now flavoured to enhance the pleasure during oral sex.
* Lubrication: most condoms are now lubricated with one thing or another, and this is normally indicated on the packet. Nonoxynol 9 is a popular spermicidal lubricant, particularly in the UK. This offers enhanced protection against pregnancy and STDs, but some users do find that this lubricant is an irritant.

There are many lubricants which can be used in conjunction with dry, un-lubricated condoms, but make sure **only** to use water-based lubricants. Baby oil, petroleum jelly and corn oil can strip a condom of its strength in just a few minutes.

"Use the new ribbed Excalibur for extra stimulation and sensitivity during intercourse."

THE LOW
DOWN BEFORE
YOU GO DOWN

* There were 140 million condoms used in the UK in 1990, compared with 102 million in 1982 - an increase of 37%. The man is now recovering in a hospital on the outskirts of Birmingham.
* In 1991 that figure crept up again to 144 million condoms, used by an estimated 1.6 million men.
* An average purchaser will use an estimated 102 condoms per year; not all at once, but two a week!
* 48% of condoms are purchased from the chemist in the UK. Pub vending machines are the next most popular place to buy. Around 7% of condoms are still obtained from the Family Planning Clinic.

- THE BRANDS WE EXAMINED

* 46% of men aged 16-20 use condoms to protect themselves against sexually transmitted diseases, and HIV/Aids.

* Men in London favour the condom more than men in other parts of the country. A recent survey showed that 35% of fellas in the capital have used condoms in the past three months, compared with 22% of Yorkshiremen!

* Durex launched the first sexual health information service in the UK as long ago as 1952. It still distributes over 2 million leaflets every year.

* The British Standard for condoms was introduced in 1989. It states that condoms must be either 48mm wide and 150mm long, or 52mm wide and 160mm long. They should also not be less than 0.04mm thick. Manufacturers conforming to these among other quality standards receive the special kitemark, British Standard BS 3704.

"Actually Mum the condom is the only thing that met British Standard."

- THE BRANDS WE EXAMINED

Abroad, it's a confusing picture when it comes to guaranteeing standards although things are improving. There are over 30 different national standards operating all over the world, and tests conducted during the manufacturing process vary enormously; some condoms are not tested at all during manufacture.

The International Standards Organisation introduced a voluntary standard for condoms in 1990, and the EC is currently working on a European standard.

USERS COME CLEAN IN CONDOM SURVEY

* Leading UK women's monthly magazine *Elle* conducted a frank sex survey among its readers in Spring 1992, in conjunction with Durex.
- 90% of respondents said that they had used condoms at some time.
- 18% have condoms with them all the time.
- 77% claimed that they would refuse to sleep with a new partner without a condom.
- 30% of women in the survey said that they 'prefer' condoms.
- And, when asked what the primary reason for using condoms is they replied: protection against STDs, 84%; birth control, 63%; and lack of medical side effects, 63%.

BIG IN CONDOMS.

LRC Products claims to be the world's biggest manufacturer of branded condoms.

"Darling do you have to bring your work home?"

Perhaps better known as the London Rubber Company, the manufacturer began life in 1915.

Its most famous brand is Durex, first used in 1932. According to the company the name is drawn from the brands' three major characteristics: durability, reliability, and excellence.

Today, Durex has an estimated 78% share of the UK market, a market it has now dominated for 50 years.

CONDOMS CLOG UP MACCLESFIELD

Drainage experts in the Macclesfield area have put the huge increase in drain blockages in the area down to thousands of used condoms.

A local drain spokesman told *The Sport* newspaper: "Since Aids there's been a dramatic increase in blockages."

The town's Family Planning Clinic commented that it was very happy if people in the area are using condoms in such large numbers.

NATIONAL CONDOM WEEK.

The 1992 National Condom Week took place in August, and is now firmly established as a regular part of the British Safety Council's annual Safe Sex campaign.

This last promotion focused on women, although the safe sex message was naturally aimed at everyone. The 1992 motto urged people to 'Slip Into Something Safe And Sexy'.

DUREX ASSURE

Manufacturer: Durex/LRC Products Ltd.

Packaging: Discreet dappled box of three condoms targeted at 'responsible' women. The condoms are blister packed in two easy-to-carry boxes of three condoms.

Special features: Coral coloured, teat ended and spermicidally lubricated with ASL these condoms are clearly designed for women who are not in a stable relationship, but who want to carry precautionary condoms discreetly.

Good Condom Guide Rating: Fun, Functional.

DUREX AROUSER

Manufacturer: Durex/LRC Products Ltd.

Packaging: Macho black and red packet of three.

Special features: These Arousers are ribbed for heightened pleasure. They are spermicidally lubricated with ASL and nonoxynol 9, and coral coloured. Certainly worth a shot in the dark.

Good Condom Guide Rating: Fun, Functional.

DUREX GOLD

Manufacturer: Durex/LRC Products Ltd.

Packaging: Yellow and gold. Packet of three plain ended condoms.

Special features: 'Quality, luxury, security'. Yes, it could be an advertisement for a bank, and I suppose it is in a way! Spermicidally lubricated with nonoxynol 9, these extra long gold coloured johnnies are top of the stocking fillers.

Good Condom Guide Rating: Fun, Functional.

DUREX EXTRA SAFE

Manufacturer: Durex/LRC Products Ltd.

Packaging: Boxed in packets of three, 12 or 18, which stress the 'extra safe' aspect of these terrific old faithfuls.

Special features: Everything you would expect to keep yourself out of trouble, including the spermicidal lubricant ASL with nonoxynol 9 for 'added protection'. These smoothies are the top selling brand of condom in the UK; the ideal family planning condom. Coral coloured, anatomically shaped. Extra Safe easily passed our 'rigid testing'.

Good Condom Guide Rating: Functional.

DUREX SAFE PLAY BLACK
Manufacturer: Durex/ LRC Products Ltd.

Packaging: Black and red packet of two hinting of a naughty evening in.

Special features: As the name suggests these first rate condoms are jet black, lightweight and teat ended. They are also lubricated with ASL. A real turn-on according to our female experts who think that black is beautiful. But, they're not very easy to find and put on in the dark!

Good Condom Guide Rating: Fun, Functional.

DUREX ELITE
Manufacturer: Durex/LRC Products Ltd.

Packaging: Premium box of 12 in a powder blue box with a yacht on the front; obviously a brand for semen!

Special features: Lubricated with a greater concentration of spermicide, this condom is smooth with a nipple end, delivering 'ultimate sensitivity, ultimate protection'.

Good Condom Guide Rating: Functional.

- THE BRANDS WE EXAMINED

DUREX SAFE PLAY MINTY

Manufacturer: Durex/LRC Products Ltd.

Packaging: Cool black and green box, packed in units of two.

Special features: Spermicidally lubricated with ASL, lightweight and teat ended. A top notch condom for those of you who like to be seen in green, this minty version is a tasty alternative to keeping strong mints in the glove compartment of your car!

Good Condom Guide Rating: Fun, Functional.

GLODOM LUMINOUS CONDOM

Manufacturer: Yorkshire Trading Ltd, Ilkley, W. Yorkshire.

Packaging: Black and green box to be seen containing one luminous Glodom.

Special features: It's the light at the end of the tunnel according to the box; whose tunnel we don't know. But, every working girl should have one in her handbag to help find her way home in the dark.

The Glodom is a novelty condom, and its effectiveness as a barrier is questionable to say the least. But, it's great fun.

For the best results from this non-lubricated white luminous monster it is best to unroll the Glodom, hold it up to the light, turn the light off and watch it glow. It's another matter when it comes to wearing the beast.

We found it an ideal ice breaker over a candle-lit supper!

Good Condom Guide Rating: Fun.

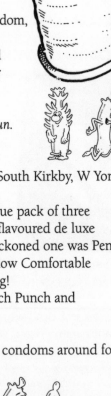

GLOW IN THE DARK TICKLERS

Manufacturer: Made by unknown company in Hong Kong, but purchased in UK.

Packaging: Perspex container holding the most gargantuan, evil looking condom we've had the pleasure to test.

Special features: This condom is awesome, and what's more it is luminous! Coloured pink and non-lubricated, this novelty condom is shaped like a flower round the edges, with nipple-like growths on the top. Wow, what a night in.

We couldn't decide whether to wear this condom, or try to grow it. Quite the most flamboyant, naughty, rude, wonderful excuse for horizontal jogging we have found. But practical, no. Wear this tickler for fancy dress only.

Good Condom Guide Rating: Flamboyant, Fun.

JIFFI COCKTAIL
Manufacturer: Jiffi Ltd, South Kirkby, W Yorks

Packaging: Black and blue pack of three selected exotic cocktail flavoured de luxe condoms; our testers reckoned one was Penis Colada, but the Long Slow Comfortable Screw was sadly missing!

Flavours include Peach Punch and Caribbean Coconut.

Special features: Some of the best flavoured condoms around for all you suckers. Also lubricated.

Good Condom Guide Rating:
Flamboyant, Fun, Functional.

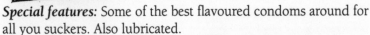

- THE BRANDS WE EXAMINED

FUNDOMS
Manufacturer: Boxer, UK

Packaging: Fun graphics on this packet of three, which nevertheless meet up to the British Standard.
The instructions for this packet of 'Big Ones - one size fits all, tiddlers to donkeys' plonkers' reads:

Fitting instructions
* Soften condom in boiling water.
* Lubricate with axle grease.
* Using a shoe horn or tyre lever, force the big willy into stretched out condom.
* Remove from boiling water.
   Should now have the appearance of a lightly cooked boil in the bag bacon joint.

Sex instructions
* Get into standing up position
* Walk slowly forward (using wheelbarrow as support if necessary)
* Walk slowly backward
* Repeat until partner is a) satisfied b) dead c) dead satisfied.

Removal instructions
Gently immerse the equipment into a bucket of caustic soda, acid or Fosters lager. After five minutes, check to see 1) if condom is still on 2) if willy is still on.

Special features: It's the packaging that makes this brand. The condoms themselves are functional.

Good Condom Guide
Rating: Functional.

ENORMEX

Manufacturer: Jarroy of London

Packaging: Novelty pack of one 'big boy extra large' - the super sheath for super men and perhaps the largest condom in the world! ...for fun only of course.

Special features: As the pack says - 'to ensure maximum protection from conception this product has been rigorously tested on an African bull elephant before being rinsed out, rerolled and packed'.

Great fun present for the man who has everything, and thinks he's well built.

Good Condom Guide Rating: Fun.

"Sorry I tired myself out opening the packet."

JIFFI EXCITER

Manufacturer: Duravend Ltd, South Kirkby, W. Yorkshire.

Packaging: Packet is quick to note that this one is for amusement only, and not to be used in the serious business of contraception, or as a barrier against STDs for that matter. Packet of one, and because it's re-usable, that's enough.

Special Features: 'Experience new ecstasy' with the Jiffi Exciter. Pretty in pink, frightening, fun!

Our laid back testing team reckons that this was designed by a young farmer with nothing to milk. It looks more like a mutant cow's udder than the mouse we think it's meant to resemble, and feels like one too. Outrageous novelty buy.

Good Condom Guide Rating: Fun.

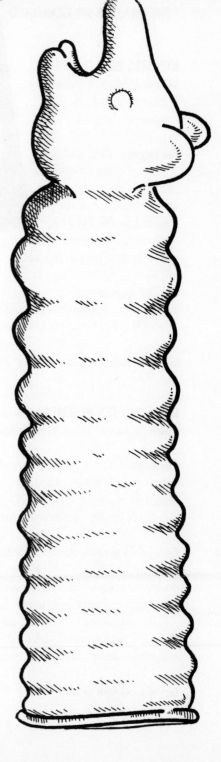

- THE BRANDS WE EXAMINED

KRYSTEL GOLD MEDAL

Manufacturer: Campbell Turner Health Care Products.

Packaging: Blue and gold packet of three smooth condoms with non-spermicidal lubricant. Rather low quality packaging compared with many brands on the market.

Special Features:
Transparent, nipple ended condom presented in a rather feminine pink sachet.

Good Condom Guide Rating: Functional.

LADY MATES PURSE PACK

Manufacturer: Mates Healthcare Ltd, Surbiton.

Packaging: Discreet is the name of the game with this brand which comes in soft pastel coloured packaging. Once the outer film is removed from the box, nobody would ever guess there are condoms inside - unless you already know it's a packet of three!

Special Features: Box is a great plus point for the easily embarrassed female purchaser. Note that these are 'ordinary' condoms targeted at the female buyer, not the much talked about revolutionary new female condoms just coming onto the market.
Lady Mates are contoured, and have a nipple or teat end. They are clear, and spermicidally lubricated.
Buyers can be three times a lady with this pack of three!

Good Condom Guide Rating: Functional.

- THE BRANDS WE EXAMINED

LE CONDOM

Manufacturer: Sagami Rubber
Industries Co Ltd, Tokyo, Japan.

Packaging: Stylish, designer
packaging. Take off the outer film
wrap of this abstract designer packet
of five condoms, and there's just a smart box - très discret. Among
stiff competition these are top notch.

Special Features: Le Condoms are quality, form-fitted, and
'Feelarama' textured, which means that they have lots of little dots
on them for 'your partner's added pleasure'. They are also lubricated.
   The manufacturer, Sagami, is one of the leading condom
companies in the world, and is claiming that Le Condom is what
the stylish Euro gent is wearing on his willy. These condoms
launched in 1991.

Good Condom Guide Rating: Flamboyant,
Fun, Functional.

MATES PLAYMATES

Manufacturer: Mates Healthcare Ltd, Surbiton (manufactured in
USA).

Packaging: Packet of three coloured
condoms in standard Mates box
lubricated with nonoxynol 9.

Special Features: Fun red, yellow
and blue form-fit condoms with a
nipple end.

Good Condom
Guide Rating:
Fun, Functional.

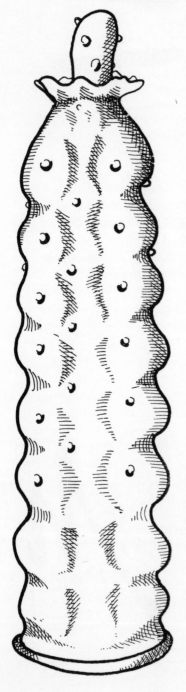

YAGO FRENCH TICKLER

Manufacturer: Unknown, but purchased in the UK.

Packaging: Box of one 'original pink French Tickler'.

Special Features: Naughty but nice novelty French Tickler, wearing a tutu on the teat. Ribs, dots.... oh la, la!

Good Condom Guide Rating: *Flamboyant, Fun.*

RUBBERS

Manufacturer: Yorkshire Trading Ltd, Ilkley, W.Yorkshire.

Packaging: Yellow and black box of three rubbers.

Special Features: Lubricated, and fruit flavoured but not a particularly tasty treat. In fact, we were not quite sure what the flavours were.

The condoms were certainly sweet smelling, but the meat eaters on our testing panel did not seem too sure about this fruity feast.

Good Condom Guide Rating:
Fun, Functional.

STEALTH CONDOMS
Manufacturer: Aegis, England.

Packaging: Pack of three multi-coloured novelty condoms boxed in a packet the shape of a Stealth Bomber, with illustration to match.

Special Features: With these on, the pack says 'they'll never see you coming!'
    Another fun gift.

Good Condom Guide Rating: Fun

- THE BRANDS WE EXAMINED

RED STRIPE

Manufacturer: Yorkshire Trading Ltd, Ilkley, W.Yorkshire.

Packaging: Red and powder blue pack of three 'protectors'.

Special Features: These new Red Stripes are 'extra strong' for safer sex according to the packet, which congratulates the purchaser for buying this brand. 'Red Stripe has for several years been known as the strong, lubricated protector with added strength without loss of sensitivity' it goes on to add. Strange, since none of our testers were familiar with the brand! But, in all fairness, our Red Stripes were strong during a stiff testing.

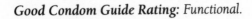

Good Condom Guide Rating: Functional.

GLO WORM

Manufacturer: Made in Thailand by Chinteik Hygiene. Distributed in UK by WOW (UK).

Packaging: Eye-catching packet of one glow-in-the-dark condom.

Special Features: There was so much lubricant on this smooth condom that our tester commented he might have slipped out of bed! Luckily he hung on in there, and was still able to keep up the momentum even after exposing the Glo Worm to a direct light source for around two minutes to make it glow.

After all the expectation - and bearing in mind the overzealous portions of gunge on the condom itself - we were disappointed. The condom nevertheless conforms to the British Standard 3704, according to the packaging, and yes it did glow!

Good Condom Guide Rating: Functional

TOUMING BIYUNTAO (TRANSPARENT CONDOM)

Manufacturer: Guilinrujiaochang - Guilin Emulsion Factory.

Packaging: Boxed in packs of ten, and supplied in one of three sizes; 35mm, 33mm and 31mm.

   We steered the middle course and gave a stiff test to the 33mm variant. But, of course, it was a little embarrassing measuring myself in the shop. The assistant must have thought I was thick or something.

Special Features: None. Very, very boring. Very, very practical if you don't fall asleep first (perhaps that's the idea?).

Good Condom Guide Rating: Functional, Feeble

JELLIA SKINS

Manufacturer: Unknown, but made in China.

Packaging: Brown and white box, packed in threes. Dull and uninteresting, but flashed 'ready for instant use'.

Special Features: Lubricated with 'hygienic jelly' but no ice cream. A straight up and down prophylactic.

Good Condom Guide Rating: Functional.

BY JINXIANGPAI BIYUNTAO (GOLDEN FLAVOUR BRAND)

Manufacturer: Shanghai Rujiao Chang - Shanghai Emulsion Factory.

Packaging: Boxed in tens (of millions!) these condoms come in four sizes: Large, 35mm; Medium, 33mm; Small, 31mm; and, Smaller, 29mm! The pack recommends that buyers choose the right size.

Special Features: None! The Chinese like to play it straight. The ultimate functional condom for a country with over a billion inhabitants.

Good Condom Guide Rating: Functional, Feeble

FRANCE

VIVE LA FRANCE

* Condom users in France want the instructions in the packets to be in the form of explicit photographs rather than the more usual drawings. And, they also want more humour and eroticism on the instruction leaflets according to a new survey in French magazine *50 Millions De Consommateurs*.

* French condom manufacturers have only had to come up to standard in the last few years. The country's standards for manufacture and packaging were introduced in 1985, but only became law in 1988.

* The French may be renowned for being the world's best lovers, but they are certainly not the world's most dedicated users of condoms. It seems that many French hommes believe that it is enough protection to have a condom in their pocket, without

using it, in the same way as a St Christopher helps protect the traveller!

* Only 9% of French with an active sex life use condoms regularly. That compares with around 37% of the British, 50% of the Canadians and 69% of the Japanese.

* The French have an awesome reputation as lovers, as we note, but a lot of it appears to be a myth.

Fewer than 20% put love top of their list of thoughts after a hard day at work. In fact, cycling and trips to the cinema are further up the scale of importance.

* Until 1986 the contract cleaning company looking after the area covering the red light district outside Paris, the huge Bois De Boulogne forest, tidied up once a week.

But, in the last few years such has been the increase in prostitution and the use of condoms that there is now a company employed just to clean up the huge number of condoms that are generated every day!

Some prostitutes using the area even help the cleaners with their massive task of keeping the wood clean by putting the 'instruments of their work' in plastic bags, and hanging them on nearby trees to be collected!

- THE BRANDS WE EXAMINED

COME TO CONDOM

Look on the bright side. At least you don't have to live in Condom, an old town in Armagnac in the Gers department in France, which dates back to the sixteenth century.

The town is on Baïse stream, about 20 miles south west of Agen-sur-Garonne. Its local specialities include armagnac, cereals, fruits and poultry, but when it comes to condoms, Condom comes nowhere.

CONDOMS BY COMPUTER

The French can now order their condoms 24 hours a day, every day of the year on their computers at home.

Condom customers can order their favourite French Letter by dialling up the condom hotline on their Minitel computer at home. Deliveries are made within 48 hours of the order being placed, so you've got to think ahead.

But, for the bashful French who don't want to visit the local chemist or supermarket for their condoms, this new way of ordering from a catalogue really comes into its own.

Customers dialling up the Minitel service can even ask which condoms are available, how to use them, and up-to-date news from the world of condoms.

Most French now have the Minitel service on-line at home. But for tourists wanting to place an order you can get onto the system by dialling '3615' on your nearest Minitel computer. Tap in the 'Preserv' code, followed by your order. The screen will prompt you on what to order, and how to pay, so don't panic! And, by the way *preservatif* is French for condom.

DUO GRIS

Manufacturer: Unknown.

Packaging: Box of ten, sold in chemists.

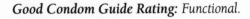

Special Features: This condom is not lubricated, but comes with a separate sachet of lubricant. Form-fit, without a nipple end.

This condom is particularly popular among the French gay community, as it is thicker than normal. For heterosexuals wanting a condom that's able to stand up to a bit of rough and tumble this would do the job, but could be a bit too thick - it really is a bit like wearing a welly.

Good Condom Guide Rating: Functional.

DURAPAC LOVE

Manufacturer: Carrefour supermarkets' own brand. Ganex-Exportex-Gani.

Packaging: Box of a dozen blister packed condoms specially for the supermarket shelf. Packaging features a couple kissing in the sun shadowed by palm trees in the background. Some clearly like it hot!

Special Features: Natural, smooth, very well lubricated, and popular with the French market. No smell, which is a plus point.

Good Condom Guide Rating: Functional.

- THE BRANDS WE EXAMINED

KHONDOMZ

Manufacturer: La Redoute, mail order catalogue.

Packaging: Box of 25 set us back over £12 - no wonder the French are not very keen on using condoms!

Special Features:
Lubricated, nipple ended. Natural colour. Very fine.

Good Condom Guide Rating: Functional.

COME QUICK   "I've been invited to France later on this year"
"Have you?"
"Yes, I got a French letter just this morning with 'come' in it!"

MANIX SUPER

Manufacturer: Manix, Okamoto, Japan.

Packaging: Box designed like the pocket in a pair of jeans. Packed in 12s, and sold in chemists.

Special Features: Pink, lubricated. Very fine, and also very strong. One of the most popular brands in France, particularly among prostitutes!

Good Condom Guide Rating:
Fun, Functional.

- THE BRANDS WE EXAMINED

PROPHYLTEX SN SPECIAL
Manufacturer: Prophyltex. Laboratories Radiatex.

Packaging: Dull grey and green box of 12, purchased in
a local chemist.

Special Features: Lubricated, green condoms.

Good Condom Guide Rating: Fun, Functional.

R3 EXCELLENT
Manufacturer: MAPA GmbH, Germany.

Packaging: Smoochy couple on pink packet is a turn-off on this box
of five German-made condoms, found on sale in the heart of Paris.

Special Features: 'Long act for man' says the
box, which is evidently meant to indicate
that the condoms are lubricated with a de-
sensitiser to delay the magic moment. If only
they'd said that in the first place!
   Fine, transparent condom that does its
job, albeit slowly!

*Good Condom Guide
Rating: Functional.*

STYMULEVE
Manufacturer: Prophyltex. Laboratories Radiatex.

Packaging: Boring, boring box of 12 sold in chemists.

Special Features: Ribbed, lubricated, natural colour, nipple ended.
The ribbing on this condom irritated our testers, and far from
enhancing the pleasure, it purely served as a reminder that the
condom was on.

Good Condom Guide Rating:
Functional.

THE BIGGEST IN THE EC!

* Germany is the biggest healthcare market in the European Community, and sales of condoms are expanding rapidly.

* Sports doctors in Germany are concerned that some women athletes are concealing condoms containing 'clean' urine samples inside their bodies in a bizarre effort to beat the drug tests now commonplace in the athletics world.

It's well known of course that Germans buy their condoms in packets of six - one for each day of the week except Sunday.

In Italy, they buy in packets of eight - one for each day of the week, and two for Sunday.

In Britain, on the other hand, buyers normally purchase a packet of 12....one for each month of the year!

BILLY BOY COLOURED

Manufacturer: MAPA GmbH, Zeven.

Packaging: Strikingly boxed in packets of four or more depending on the Billy Boy variant. The brand comes in coloured, dotted, extra lube and flavoured varieties.

Special Features: The Good Condom Guide road tested Billy Boy coloured. We like to be seen in green, but red is better in bed! Lubricated and teat ended.

Good Condom Guide Rating: Fun, Functional.

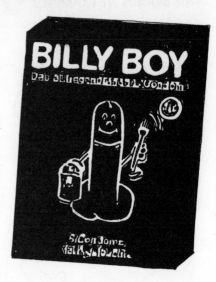

ANTI BABY CONDOM

Manufacturer: Blaüsiegel, MAPA GmbH, Zeven.

Packaging: Boxed in packets of 12.

Special Features: These Blaüsiegel condoms are very popular in Germany and this Anti Baby Condom gets straight to the point - no nonsense! The condoms themselves are lubricated, and contain a spermicide.

Good Condom Guide Rating: Functional.

- THE BRANDS WE EXAMINED

COLOR EXTRA FEUCHT

Manufacturer: Rimbacher Gummiwaren-Fabrik GmbH, Rimbach, Germany.

Packaging: 1960s design comes back to haunt us on this packet of six coloured condoms purchased from a vending machine in Berlin Airport.

Special features: Thin, smooth and lubricated. They call the colours 'fresh and cheeky' on the packet, and they are all different.

Good Condom Guide Rating: Fun, Functional.

"Darling, it's a red letter day."

- THE BRANDS WE EXAMINED

H.T SPECIAL

Manufacturer: MAPA GmbH, Zeven.

Packaging: Black and white box of three.

Special Features: Extra strong for those big strapping rough German boys. No chance of these breaking, I can tell you. Not unless you're a donkey. H.T Special is a veritable raincoat.

Good Condom Guide Rating: Functional.

YOUNG HEARTS

Manufacturer: Ritex.

Packaging: Smart pink boxes with hearts on containing six lubricated condoms.

Special Features: Coral coloured, but with no other distinguishing features worth noting.

Good Condom Guide Rating: Functional.

THE EURO CONDOM

Manufacturer: Unknown.

Packaging: Purchased as a single condom with the EC flag emblazoned on the wrapper.

Special Features: The Eurocrats will find this dark blue lubricated international condom hard to beat. Fun for those holiday encounters where it's difficult to converse in anything other than the language of love.

Good Condom Guide Rating: Fun.

GEFÜHLSECHT

Manufacturer: London Rubber Co, Munich.

Packaging: Lovers' scene - are they disappearing into the sunset for a quickie? (or two, as there are two condoms in the packet).

Special Features: Heavily lubricated, and transparent.

Good Condom Guide Rating: Functional.

HONEYMOON SUPER STIMULATION

Manufacturer: MAPA GmbH, Zeven.

Packaging: Small, discreet box of two condoms.

Special Features: Lubricated condoms with a cheeky dotted shaft to give 'the super stimulation that your partner will appreciate'. Nice product that certainly tickled our fancy. Good fun.

Honeymoon brand also comes in 'Double Safe', 'Extra Thin', 'Ribbed' and de-sensitising 'Super Delay' - but it was too late for me.

Good Condom Guide Rating: Fun, Functional.

JAMAICA

CONDOM USE IN THE CARIBBEAN AND LATIN AMERICA

Condom use for family planning among women of reproductive age:

	% Using any method	% Using condoms
* Jamaica	55%	9%
Brazil	66	2
Colombia	63	2
Costa Rica	70	13
Dominican Republic	50	1
El Salvador	47	2
Grenada	31	8
Guatamala	23	1
Honduras	41	2
Mexico	53	2
Paraguay	45	2
Trinidad and Tobago	53	12

From Population Reports, series H No 8. Barrier Methods, September 1990. Published by the Population Information Program, The Johns Hopkins University, Baltimore.

SULTAN

Manufacturer: Ansell Incorporated, Dothan, Alabama, USA.

Packaging: Given away free of charge by the Jamaican Family Planning Association, these Sultan condoms are flow wrapped in rather dull red and white packaging.

Special Features: Smells of a 'fish supper' said our team of condom connoisseurs. My Jamaican friend added that the condoms are "irie" (that's 'cool' for the uninitiated).

Good Condom Guide Rating: Functional.

JAPAN

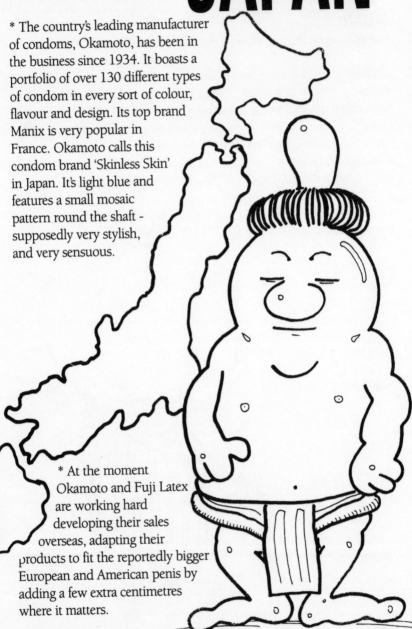

* The country's leading manufacturer of condoms, Okamoto, has been in the business since 1934. It boasts a portfolio of over 130 different types of condom in every sort of colour, flavour and design. Its top brand Manix is very popular in France. Okamoto calls this condom brand 'Skinless Skin' in Japan. It's light blue and features a small mosaic pattern round the shaft - supposedly very stylish, and very sensuous.

* At the moment Okamoto and Fuji Latex are working hard developing their sales overseas, adapting their products to fit the reportedly bigger European and American penis by adding a few extra centimetres where it matters.

* At home in Japan, the pill is unpopular. The condom is by far and away the most important method of birth control. Indeed, the 120 million Japanese use more

condoms than the Americans and Europeans put together! And what's more, all the condoms in Japan are manufactured by the Japanese who claim the highest standards of manufacture in the world.

* Hormonal contraceptives are not available in Japan. Here 45% of all couples - 69% of all family planning users - rely on condoms.

* In Japan nearly all boxes of condoms are disguised to look like packets of bath salts to help shy Japanese women overcome the embarrassment of buying them.
   And what can they buy? How about a packet of Almighty, or Here Comes The Giants?

* Japanese condom manufacturer Fuji Latex has a head office built in the shape of a condom.
   The cylindrical tower is right in the centre of Tokyo.

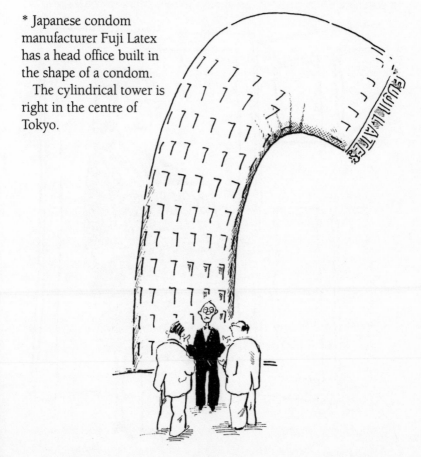

CONDOM CALLING JAPANESE STYLE

Just like the old Avon ladies in the UK, condoms are often sold door-to-door in downtown Japan homing in on shy housewives.

Sex is still an awkward subject in Japan, and the door-to-door condom sellers - known as 'skin ladies' - find their targets easy prey.

Some women have been known to happily buy a year's supply of condoms at one go, which can cost upwards of £500. And, some have even been known to buy twice in one year - either wishful thinking, or an incredible moment of madness!

According to reports, one skilled skin lady recently made a killing when she sold in a lifetime's supply of condoms one morning; that order came to 10,000 condoms.

Men rarely buy condoms in Japan. Here it is still the woman's job to purchase them, and for that matter to remember to use them.

- THE BRANDS WE EXAMINED

VISCOUNT

Manufacturer: We think this could be manufactured by Nakanishi Gomukogyo Co. Ltd, Osaka, Japan, but the single condom supplied did not indicate the manufacturer.

Packaging: Sent in to *The Good Condom Guide* from our Asian Correspondent (unused, of course!) Single, foil wrapped condom in plain wrapper with regal graphics.

Special Features: Packaging claims this brand is lubricated and scented, but we were not convinced about either claim. The rose coloured condom did not feel as though it was lubricated at all, and it only smelt of condom! But, Viscount is well ribbed.

Good Condom Guide Rating: *Functional.*

LONGCHAMP - JOY.G

Manufacturer: Sagami Rubber Industries Co, Tokyo, Japan.

Packaging: Smart, modern design box of three Japanese Johnnies.

Special Features: Slick designer foil inner packet reveals a royal blue lubricated form-fit condom. Longchamp met the *Guide's* rough strength test, and we liked the fact that the brand did not have an overpowering smell, although it was a bit greasy to the taste.

Good Condom Guide Rating: *Fun, Functional.*

- THE BRANDS WE EXAMINED

LONG LOVE

Manufacturer: Nakanishi Gomukogyo Co. Ltd, Osaka, Japan.

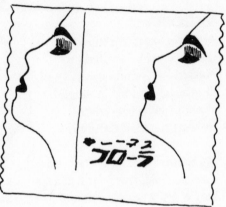

Packaging: Sent in to *The Good Condom Guide* as a single, foil wrapped condom with smart modern graphic design.

Special Features: Teat ended, lubricated with a de-sensitiser we think, and ribbed with stars and bars! Long Love is rose coloured, and great fun. The only star-studded condom for studs we found!

Good Condom Guide Rating: Fun, Functional.

EIGHT EIGHT STAR

Manufacturer: Unknown.

Packaging: Single condom packed in plain sky blue foil.

Special Features: Lubricated, rose coloured and superbly ribbed with prominent dots. Can you feel the force? We did!

Good Condom Guide Rating: Fun, Functional.

"Shall I pop down to the chemist for a packet of three?"

SKIN LESS SKIN

Manufacturer: Okamoto Industries Inc, Japan.

Packaging: Sent in to *The Good Condom Guide* for testing as a single, foil wrapped condom in very plain silver and green packaging.

Special Features: Packaging hides a fun, lightly lubricated, thin, teat ended pale blue condom which is slightly ribbed with a criss-cross ring around the head end, and raised squares towards the open end of the condom.

Good Condom Guide Rating:
Fun, Functional.

EUROGLIDER

Manufacturer: NVSH, Holland.

Packaging: International blue and yellow Euro box of 12 lubricated condoms with a 'reservoir' end, for those of you who need a little more than a teat! Perfect for the Eurovision Dong Contest.

Special Features: A real international 'in-between' the stocking filler for you and your friends. Instructions and advice in six languages as befits a Euro condom.
   Euroglider condoms conform to the quality standard enforced by Dutch law, a standard which covers all European quality requirements.

Good Condom Guide Rating: Functional.

- THE BRANDS WE EXAMINED

FUN

Manufacturer: NVSH, Den Haag.

Packaging: Boxed in packets of two, and 12 (one for each month of the year possibly).

Special Features: Fun are 'ribbelcondooms met glijmiddel' - yes, you've guessed it, lubricated and ribbed top to bottom, with just a short break for a rest in the middle. Naughty and nice, with a spermicidal lubricant.

Good Condom Guide Rating: *Fun, Functional.*

GAY SAFE

Manufacturer: NVSH, Den Haag.

Packaging: Boxed in packets of one condom, which includes a sachet of sterile lubricating jelly.

Special Features: These condoms are stronger, for obvious reasons, and dry with a water soluble lubricant included in the box. Instructions are included in two languages, Dutch and English. Good functional condoms to keep in your bottom drawer.

Good Condom Guide Rating: *Functional.*

TUTTI FRUTTI

Manufacturer: NVSH, Den Haag.

Packaging: Boxed in packets of one condom or more.

Special Features: As the name suggests Tutti Frutti comes 'met smaakje', in fruit flavours like strawberry, lemon, licorice, and banana. Very sugary flavours, a bit sickly, but then again what do you expect from a condom? It's better than the taste of latex for the suckers among you! Lubricated with nonoxynol 9.

Good Condom Guide Rating: Fun, Functional.

tutti frutti®

NVSH

CONDOOMS MET SMAAKJE,
AARDBEI, PEPERMUNT, DROP.
VOORGEVORMD, MET RESERVOIR.

HAPPY FACE

Manufacturer: Allwrap Products, Auckland (distributor).

Packaging: Big, brash packet of one. Superb bright packaging.

Special Features: Flashed '100% Pure Beef' the Happy Face condom comes straight to the point inviting users to 'Put On A Happy Face' - and why not?

   Well, the packaging is fun, but the condoms themselves are purely functional as far as our experts at the *Guide* are concerned, no more, no less.

Good Condom Guide Rating: Functional.

TROPIC

Manufacturer: Funny Love Shop. Imported by VIB A/S, Bergen, Norway.

Packaging: Boxed in units of nine condoms. Three each of three fruity flavours: lemon, banana and strawberry.

Special Features: 'Don't worry be happy' is the message on the side of the packet of these 'De Luxe Quality Kondomer', although you may not be so happy when you see the price. Tropic are certainly at the dearer end of the fruity market. The packaging is fun, and the flavours are subtle.

Good Condom Guide Rating: Fun, Functional.

SPAIN

WHAT A CHOICE
* There are now more than 60 brands of condoms on offer in Spain.

* In a novel advertisement for Spanish condom Primex in the 1980s, a woman's hand suggestively caresses a man's hand until the thumb starts to rise up like an erection, at which point the thumb is capped like a condom.

* Condoms were first advertised on Spanish television in 1986.

ANDROTEX ANATOMICO

Manufacturer: Prophyl Center SA.

Packaging: Sophisticated black and gold packet of 12 condoms for the smooth go-getting man who wants to put a little bit more into his condoms.

Special Features: This packet of transparent, nipple ended condoms are flashed 'extra-creme special', but to be honest we didn't notice the extra lubricant during testing. However, the manufacturer does highlight the exhaustive testing this brand undergoes, and the fact that they are top quality condoms.

There are good instructions in the box, which also contain some absorbing information about how the brand is tested by Androtex, complete with illustrations of inflated Johnnies.

Good Condom Guide Rating: **Functional.**

70

- THE BRANDS WE EXAMINED

SPECIAL NEWPHYLCREM
Manufacturer: Dongkuk Trading Co. Ltd.

Packaging: Picture packet featuring a smiling family of four wearing what look like clothes right out of the 1970s fashion wardrobe - we're sure it will all come back into fashion again soon! The box is blister packed for sale in supermarkets. Packaging gives the brand a sensible, practical feel, and the condoms do not disappoint.

Special Features: Lubricated, nipple ended transparent condoms designed to stop the man and woman on the front having any more nasty accidents.

Good Condom Guide Rating: Functional.

FAMILY ANATOMICAL
Manufacturer: CEX International, Spain.

Packaging: This box of a dozen condoms notes that the products inside are for family planning, so it's a bit odd that the packaging portrays a beaming family of four. But, the name of these condoms gives the game away - they're baby stoppers!

Special Features: Despite their humdrum image, these condoms performed well under a stiff test. Form-fitted, Family Anatomical shaped up well. And, what's more these baby stoppers are ribbed. 'Minimum thickness, maximum elasticity, better resistance' says the blurb, adding: 'Family prophylactics are lubricated with a thin layer of creame (their spelling not ours!) overlaid uniformly on their surface, conferring them an homogeneous, sensitive and natural sliding'.

Good Condom Guide Rating:
Fun, Functional.

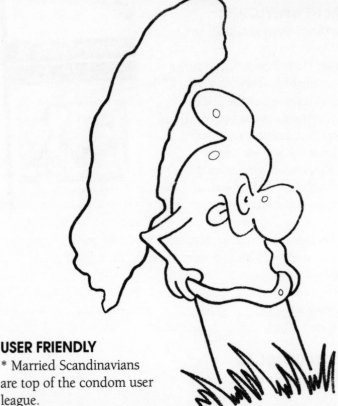

USER FRIENDLY

* Married Scandinavians are top of the condom user league.

Sweden, Denmark, and Finland all have rates of condom use among married couples over 20%. In most developing countries this figure varies between 5% and 15%, while in the USA some 11% of married couples use condoms.

* The Swedes have come up with a penis character to promote the use of condoms - Proud Pete.

Pete wears a condom, and he speaks too! Not surprisingly, he's been given the thumbs up by the Swedish government and the country's Family Planning Association.

* 1987 advertisements for top Swedish condom manufacturer RFSU showed women blowing up unwrapped condoms, then letting them fly away to the catchline: 'If he won't put it on, tell him it's off'.

- THE BRANDS WE EXAMINED

CHO-SAN

Manufacturer: Made in Japan, but distributed in Sweden by RFSU, Stockholm.

Packaging: Bright red and white wallet of ten condoms with an oriental motif on the box.

Special Features: Extra sensitive, form-fitted.

Good Condom Guide Rating: Functional.

MAMBA

Manufacturer: Made in Japan, but distributed in Sweden by RFSU, Stockholm.

Packaging: Mamba comes in a smart clever wallet of ten condoms.

Special Features: Bright yellow, tighter form-fit condoms, but with no instructions for use!

Good Condom Guide Rating: Functional.

SHOT TO PIECES

* Condom sales in the USA were increasing by between 10-15% every year in the 1980s.

Then, in November 1986, the Surgeon General called for condom use to prevent Aids, and public discussion of condoms became acceptable. As a result, budget predictions for condom sales were shot to pieces and sales rose by 50% in 1987!

* Around 14% of those using contraceptives in the USA use condoms. That compares with 21% in Spain, and 6% in France.

* Durex Group research shows that some two-thirds of high school kids in the USA claim to be having regular sexual relations. This rises to 80% by the time they move on to college. But, only 20% of them use condoms.

However, in another recent survey of American women, increases in condom use were shown to be chiefly among the unmarried.

- THE BRANDS WE EXAMINED

* American Tips, condoms designed to fit only over the glans of the penis, have had a terrible reputation for slipping off over the years. They were particularly popular in the 1930s. But, despite their dodgy reputation, they're still available today.

GET REDDY!

Reddy Health is set to launch a new female condom in the US called the Bikini Condom.

This is a soft lubricated bikini with a built-in rolled condom in the crotch.

The condom element of the bikini is automatically unrolled into the vagina by the erect penis during intercourse.

Experts say that it's coming to Europe soon.

"Hello darling I'm just trying on my new condom."

FLY RIGHT

Manufacturer: Trimensa Corp, Sun Valley. Marketed by GMHC (Gay Men's Health Crisis) New York.

Packaging: Pack of two unlubricated condoms with a sachet of ForPlay 'sensual' lubricant containing spermicide in a discreet, fun packet.

Special Features: Good 'safe sex' instructions in this packet of two which is clearly targeted at the gay community; 'you can have all the great sex you want - just be sure to make it safer'.

Good Condom Guide Rating: Functional.

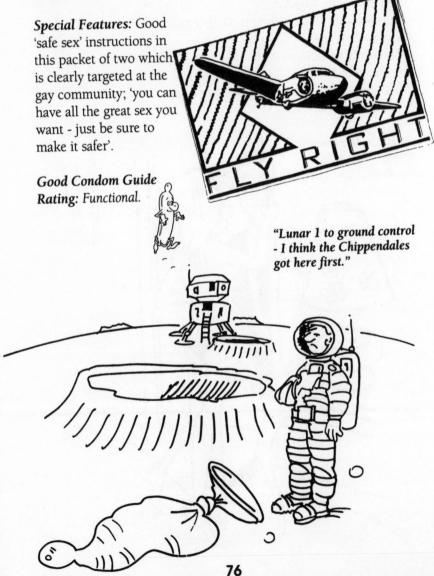

"Lunar 1 to ground control - I think the Chippendales got here first."

POWER PLAY

Manufacturer: Ansell Incorporated, Dothan, Alabama, US.

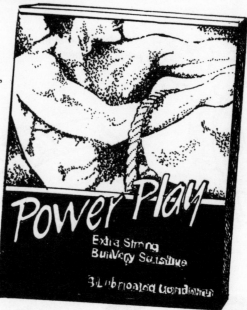

Packaging: Striking macho box claiming that Power Play are extra strong but very sensitive. Box of three lubricated condoms with spermicidal lubricant nonoxynol 9.

Special Features:
Extra strength against breakage for the big Yankee boys, but still very sensitive and light. The packaging is rude. Power Play is one of a range of six naughty but nice condoms in this range from Ansell Incorp., America's largest manufacturer of condoms.

Others in the range include *Wet N' Wild* - 'velvety smooth and stirring with natural pleasure'; *Kiss Of Mint* - 'tantalisingly fragrant'; *Rough Rider* - 'studded up and down and all the way round...pleasure points pulsating with excitement'; and, *Erotica* - 'row after row of sensuous ribbing, raised to excite...a favourite among men, and an even bigger favourite among women'.

Bareback is also in this range, and is reviewed on page 79.

As for Power Play, there's plenty of protection here - strength and a good spermicide.

Good Condom Guide Rating:
Fun, Functional.

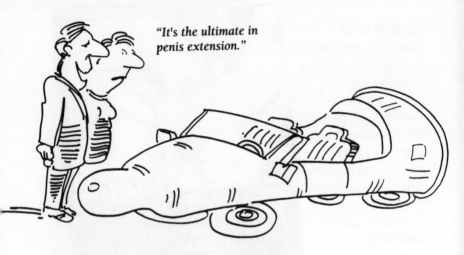

"It's the ultimate in penis extension."

LICKS

Manufacturer: Licks International, San Francisco (distributor).

Packaging: Colourful no-nonsense box leaves the buyer in no doubt as to what these tasty condoms are for. Box of three fruit flavoured condoms contains one each of banana, passion fruit, and cherry.

Special Features: The box claims the flavours are 'natural fruit', but wow they are strong flavours! '100% natural latex condoms' to 'tantalise your taste....a refreshing experience'. Really a novelty brand.

Good Condom Guide Rating: Fun.

- THE BRANDS WE EXAMINED

MAGNUM LARGER SIZE

Manufacturer: Carter Products, New York (distributor).

Packaging: Black and gold box highlighting that the Magnum brand is 'Larger Size' - just right for the American six-shooters. Three big boy condoms in a box, packed in gold foil. It leaves you in no doubt that you're in for something special.

Special Features: Magnum is clearly the brand to keep in your wallet to impress potential partners. Then, of course, you'll need to swap the Magnum over for a smaller brand when the light is off later on!

Magnum is lubricated and certainly larger, but I wonder whether it really does make much difference. After all the 'ordinary' condom is big enough to hold the average whale's penis, let alone a mere man's. One thing is for sure. Magnum is good for the ego, if you've got one big enough.

Good Condom Guide Rating:
Flamboyant, Fun, Functional.

BAREBACK

Manufacturer: Ansell Incorporated, Dothan, Alabama, US.

Packaging: Naughty, seductive nude sells this 'super sensitive' packet of three lubricated condoms.

Special Features: The box says that Bareback is 'almost like wearing nothing at all.....like riders who mount without a saddle'. What?!

Very strong, very light, very sensitive....for those who 'really

want to feel close'. Good marketing for a very good, fun brand. One of six in the rude range (see also Power Play).

Good Condom Guide Rating: *Fun, Functional.*

BEYOND

Manufacturer: Made in Tokyo by Okamoto Industries for distribution in the West, especially the USA.

Packaging: Elegant pink, blue and gold box of three green Sheerlon, lightly lubricated condoms packed in a classic, distinctive blue and gold inner 'tamper evident' foil.

Special Features: Classy packaging, green, and made of Sheerlon – 'thinner, super strong and silky soft for a sensuous natural experience.' The manufacturer claims it is the closest thing to nothing at all.

Sheerlon is a strong durable material which means that the condoms can be made much thinner than is the case with conventional latex rubber, which gives them the skin-like feel. And, while Beyond is a little more expensive, the experience is worth it.

Good Condom Guide Rating: *Flamboyant, Fun, Functional.*

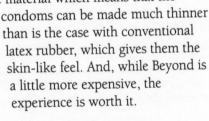

- THE BRANDS WE EXAMINED

KIMONO PLUS

Manufacturer: Distributed by Mayer Laboratories, Oakland. Manufactured by Sagami Rubber, Tokyo, Japan.

Packaging: Oriental-feel yellow and gold box of three Kimono Plus condoms.

Special Features: Ultra thin, form-fit, transparent, and natural latex. The condoms also feature the spermicidal lubricant nonoxynol 9. Good instructions are a bonus: 'After sex...try not to spill semen (cum). Throw the used condom away. Wash up'. Not even a cuddle or a cigarette!

Mayer Labs claims to be the maker of Europe's most popular condoms, according to the packet.

Good Condom Guide Rating: Functional.

YOUNG LOVERS

Manufacturer: Who knows! No manufacturer's name in sight. No country of origin. And no sign of any international, British or other standards.

Packaging: A couple of young lovers heavy petting on the packet of three lubricated condoms. The packaging says that the condoms are electronically tested and hygienically sealed. But, with no manufacturer's mark, no instructions, no anything, this brand caused some concern among our testing panel.

Special Features: Young Lovers got the thumbs down from our couple on the job. When we tried the brand, the condom split. We also felt that there was too much lubricant.

Good Condom Guide Rating: Functional.

- THE BRANDS WE EXAMINED

GOLD CIRCLE

Manufacturer: Lyndhurst, New Jersey. Distributed by the Safetex Corporation.

Packaging: Ultra smart, sleek packet. Upmarket black and gold box of three condoms individually packed in gold coins, just like the chocolate gold coins we get under the Christmas tree.

Special Features: The packaging and presentation is brilliant, but the condoms themselves do not quite live up to the promise of mystery the box gives the brand.

Gold Circle condoms are non-lubricated with a reservoir end, and are 'ultra-thin', coloured white. A condom for special 'gold' occasions - golden weddings perhaps!

Good Condom Guide Rating: *Flamboyant, Functional.*

HARMONY

Manufacturer: Made in Tokyo by Okamoto Industries Inc for distribution in the West, particularly the USA.

Packaging: Red and blue packet of three skin-less skin Harmony latex condoms.

Special Features: Thumbs up for Harmony from Japan. We know these Japanese condoms are rigorously machine tested, and in our more simple testing they did not disappoint. Harmony is a rose coloured lightly lubricated condom with a reservoir end. It also feels very fine and light, hence the skin-less skin tag. And there isn't too much of an aroma or nasty taste with this brand - which makes a nice change.

Good Condom Guide Rating: *Fun, Functional.*

FLANCY 3000
Manufacturer: Okamoto Industries, Tokyo, Japan.

Packaging: Awful 1960s flower-power packaging, holding three Flancy condoms. The packaging really lets the brand down.

Special Features: Excellent textured rose design on the superb, scented pink condom! You can't see it, or feel it in the dark...but it's there. It's a good idea, but the packaging, and marketing of this fun brand on-pack could have been so much better.

Good Condom Guide Rating: Fun, Functional.

PRIME
Manufacturer: Ansell Incorporated, Dothan, Alabama, US.

Packaging: Simple blue and white packet of three, from America's largest manufacturer of sleeping bags for mice.

Special Features: Lubricated with SK-70 'for natural action'; our experts were not too keen on the smell.

Good Condom Guide Rating: Functional.

* An estimated 45 million couples use condoms worldwide.

* Around 6,000 million condoms may have been used worldwide in 1990.

* Japan is the biggest single user. Here, around 70% of couples who use contraceptives use condoms.

* In stark contrast, condom use is very low in Africa, the Middle East and Latin America.

INTERNATIONAL RESCUE
* If you asked for a packet of Durex in Australia, you'd probably be given a roll of adhesive tape!

"Are you sure it should be this sticky Darling?"

* Over to Canada where burger chain McDonald's recently obtained a court order preventing a Montreal sex shop from retailing 'McCondoms', claiming that the store was using its proprietary 'Mc' prefix.

Newspapers report that the sex shop has now been ordered to destroy all its unsold McCondoms. However, one local comedian has suggested that the burger giant buy up the condom stock as they may taste better than the hamburgers!

"Mummy I think Daddy is having the free shake as well."

* Going out to dinner in Odense, Denmark? Then watch out for after dinner condoms!

In some restaurants condoms are now being served with the after dinner coffee instead of the usual mints.

The move has been made in support of the local safe sex campaign, not as some of the diners suggested, as an invitation to clientele to 'come again'.

"Last time I was here I had a rather delicious ribbed with lubrication."

* It's reported that two thirds of the 27 or so condoms available on the Hong Kong market either leak or are not thick enough for their job.

The Consumer Council says its patience is wearing thin on this one.

* Sales of condoms in Kenya are booming as a result of the growing threat of HIV/Aids, having risen from 10,000 per month in 1986 to well over 350,000 by the end of the decade.

* The Mexicans have somehow made the link between condoms and football! They dressed up their animated new condom symbol in a football shirt to introduce him at the World Cup.

PUTTING THE STRESS ON PREVENTION

According to World Health Organisation (WHO) planning methodology applied to men aged between 15 and 65, there are an estimated 8,000 million condoms needed for Aids prevention progammes alone!

"When I said bring him off at half-time I meant ..."

"... and what size would you like Madame?"

THE FEMALE CONDOM .... FEMIDOM

If you thought you'd seen some bizarre condoms on your travels, just wait till you come across the Femidom, the new female condom - the 'first contraceptive for women which provides a controllable method of protection against pregnancy and STDs'.

Recently launched all over Europe, the manufacturer Chartex International says Femidom is easy to use: 'simply insert the Femidom in a similar way to a tampon'. It lines the natural contours of the vagina with a soft pliable polyurethane sheath, has an inner ring which is used for insertion and which holds the sheath in place beyond the pubic bone, and an outer ring which lies flat against the labia.

Femidom has been tested in more than 15 countries round the world as far afield as the USA, Europe, Africa, the Far East and Russia.

Unlike the boys' condom, it doesn't depend on an erection, and can be inserted before love making, and removed afterwards when it suits both partners.

Femidom is pre-lubricated and odourless.

This could be the new age welly all men have been waiting for. The ball's in your court girls!

According to some cutting early reports the Femidom is said to look rather like a 'lobster pot'.

One tester in UK men's magazine *Esquire* said that there was something "rather perverse about making love to a woman with a plastic bag sticking out", and another said that "it's also quite horribly noisy".

"It's pre-lubricated, for which read very greasy, but needs extra gunk which makes anything but a quickie a considerable labour of love and very messy," was another comment.

In conclusion, the *Esquire* testers said that it was "hellish to get started and completely useless for casual sex". But, the good thing is that it is another option....

AMERICANS FLAG NEW CONDOM BRAND DOWN!

The US patents office has refused a patent for a new American brand of red white and blue condoms called Old Glory - a well known name for the Stars and Stripes.

The brand was to have gone on the market with the catchy slogan 'Worn with pride countrywide'. The packaging intended to feature the American flag pictured in the shape of a condom, with a witty slogan 'Long may it wave'.

The Patent and Trademarks Office refused to sanction a trademark for the condoms, manufactured by the Old Glory Condom Corporation, because of the use of the US national flag. This allows it to refuse permits for 'immoral, deceptive or scandalous matter'.

THE LORDS OF LATEX

Ansell International is the world's largest manufacturer of latex products, and one of the world's top condom manufacturers.

The company employs nearly 9,000 people and sells condoms in 80 different countries.

Ansell sales in 1988-89 were worth approximately £200 million, including 7 million gross of condoms!

TRUNCHEON CLUB

Thailand has its own penis character to promote the use of condoms.

The country has already armed its police force with condoms for use among the population, nicknaming the campaign 'Cops and Rubbers'.

"Excuse me sir, could you blow into this."

"Your condoms or your life."

CONDOM DEATH THREAT TO CHEMISTS!

Sikh militants in the Punjab have been trying to ban condoms in an effort to help boost their population.

Sikhs are trying to produce as many young 'soldiers' as possible to help fight the Indian government for a special Sikh homeland in Khalistan.

And, the issue has become so important that some chemists are now being threatened with death if they sell condoms!

OF CABBAGES AND CONDOMS

Thailand is trying to clean up its act as the sex capital of the world, and Thai Cabinet member Mechai Viravaidya - half Scot, half Thai - is leading the crusade.

Mr Viravaidya owns a restaurant called Cabbages & Condoms, and says that he wants condoms to become as much a part of the Thai's shopping list as the average fresh vegetable!

CONDOMS FEATURED
IN THE GUIDE.

SPECIALIST CONDOM SHOPS

* Condomania, 57 Rupert Street, London W1V 7HN
(071 287 2249).

* Condomania, Liverpool Palace, 6-10 Slater Street, Liverpool
L1 4BT (051 707 0189).

* Condomania, The Balcony, The Corn Exchange, Call Lane, Leeds
LS1 7BP (0532 446532).

And overseas:

* Condomania, 359 Bleecker Street, Greenwich Village,
New York, USA.

* Condomerie, The Reeperbahn, Hamburg, Germany.

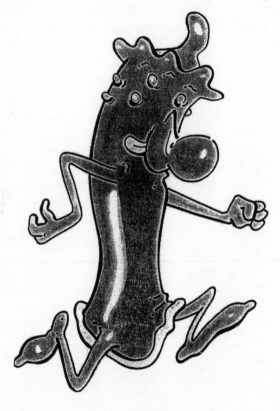